# Tiny Tales of Hope

## First Edition

Published in 2012 by Portfolio Gallery Ltd.
12 John Street, Ballymena, BT43 6DU

Printed by GPS Colour Graphics Limited

**Author Dawn McKeown**
Copyright © 2012 Dawn McKeown
info@dawnmckeownphotography.com
028 2563 2816

A catalogue record for this book is available from the British Library.

All proceeds from the sale of this book will go directly to TinyLife
Registered Charity No: XN75792/1    Company No: NI037799

International Standard Book Number:  978-0-9560095-1-7

Piglet sidled up to Pooh from behind.
'Pooh!' he whispered.
'Yes, Piglet?'
'Nothing', said Piglet, taking Pooh's paw.
'I just wanted to be sure of you.'"

~A.A. Milne

# Tiny Tales of Hope

6

# *D*ear Reader

The Rotary Club of Ballymena is delighted to have assisted with the production of this inspirational book. We try to achieve a balance between involvement with the many worldwide projects of Rotary International and providing support to our local community. As a local charity working to benefit the lives of so many babies, parents and wider families, TinyLife is certainly deserving of such assistance.

TinyLife, by giving invaluable support when it is most needed, allows families to cope with the challenges of the present and to dare to hope for the future.

This book with its stunning photography serves to remind us that no matter how physically weak and frail we might appear or how bleak the future might seem, we must always look to our inner strength and reach for tomorrow.

The emotions experienced by the families whose stories have been told have so very skillfully been captured and brought to life by Dawn McKeown - a fitting tribute to TinyLife.

I trust that you will enjoy this book as much as I have, also knowing that your financial support will be put to very good use.

James McKervill
President
Rotary Club of Ballymena

*Tiny Tales of Hope*

# I am addressing this to you. Yes, you, who surprised your parents and everyone around you and were born a little bit early.

Your mother didn't expect you early. She did everything she could to avoid it. But, it just happened. Doctors may have planned to get you out early for very good reasons or maybe Mother Nature just flicked the switch. She may have had her reasons, but she started a sequence of events that have lead to you being the unique person that you are. Many, many people were involved in trying to stop the process; deliver you, care for you, nurture you and support your parents. After birth, they could only watch on, and hope and pray that everything was going to be alright.

And if you are reading this today, then it has been!

Being born well before 9 months may have seemed like the end of the world for those who loved you but although not to be sought, it can give and in fact did give you just the unexpected and most intriguing start to your life.
Let me tell you a story...

I am an Obstetrician but I am also a Gynaecologist and so am privileged to consult with women beyond the reproductive years. Just last week, I met a woman who was 82 years old, she told me her amazing story and gave me permission to share it with you.

Sarah was born on 22nd December 1929 at 23 weeks gestation. She was born at home with the membranes round her still intact. We Irish regard this 'caul' as bringing good luck, which it did. She weighed 20 oz and was just 12 inches long. Her eyes were fussed together and she had no finger nails. She was laid on a bed of cotton wool, put in a shoe box and was placed beside the range. Her father went out and bought a new fountain pen and dropped cow's milk into her mouth at regular intervals. Olive oil was poured onto her skin daily, though not rubbed in.

When she could tolerate solids, she was prescribed (by her GP!) raw beef and liver, an orange and 4 teaspoons of Harvey's 5 star brandy every day!

Sarah thrived incredibly well on this regime and won a scholarship from school, was 3rd in the UK at mental-arithmetic and won every quiz she ever attempted. She has been as 'fit as a fiddle' all of her life and went onto have 2 sons of her own. Put simply, she never looked back at her early start in life. When I met her, she had all her faculties and was as 'sharp as a tack'.

*So, remember, what ever happens after a premature birth, you will always be a very special and unique person. And whatever you do in life, never give up and always have and give hope, even when it seems there is none.*

Professor Jim Dornan
Chair Fetal Medicine Queen's University Belfast
Consultant Royal Jubilee Maternity Hospital

# 'I Really didn't feel like her Mum'.

Isla was born on Wednesday 6th January 2010 at 31 weeks gestation, weighing 3lbs 6oz.

I had a problem free pregnancy. The morning Isla was born, I woke up with a severe headache, had little vision and was extremely confused.

Upon arrival at the Royal Jubilee Maternity Hospital, I had an eclamptic seizure and our little girl was born by emergency section 45 minutes later.

Isla was taken straight to neonatal intensive care unit where she was on CPAP for the next 3 days. Isla was 2 days old when I got to meet her for the first time.

My vision wasn't fully restored so I was only able to hold her for 2 minutes. I was overjoyed but incredibly frightened by how small and fragile she was.

I didn't really feel like her Mum, as the nurses and doctors were doing a better job caring for her than I could'.

The hardest thing was being discharged from hospital and leaving our baby behind.

When I was pregnant, we had always imagined taking our baby home straight away, premature birth never featured in our plans.

At one point, I was readmitted to the Royal and Isla was in the Ulster special care baby unit. It was a huge strain for my husband, Richard, who would have to drive between the two hospitals.

Whilst both hospitals were wonderful, we found her time in hospital emotionally and practically draining.

Following 29 days in hospital, Isla was discharged weighing 4lb 8oz. She has now fully caught up in terms of weight and size. Initially she had feeding problems but these are now a thing of the past.

Looking back on our experience, we often wonder how we coped but it has made us stronger, as a family.

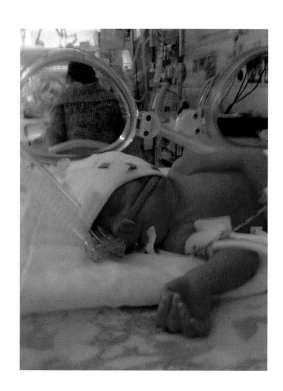

Isla Hassard
Born 31 weeks gestation, weighing 3lbs 6oz

# 'One Dad's story...'

I awoke on Saturday 7th May 2007, looking forward to a long weekend in Portugal. Jane, my wife, was 28 weeks pregnant and had been given the all-clear to fly by her GP.

She was feeling a bit 'off' and we decided to call into the Ulster Hospital Dundonald en route to the airport.

We didn't leave the hospital that night and at 1am on Tuesday 8th May 2007, Rhianna Hope Wilton came into our lives, 12 weeks earlier than expected – Portugal could wait.

The birth was a surreal experience.

Rhianna, weighing in at 2lb 8oz, said 'Hello' to the world and very briefly to Mummy and Daddy and was hurried away to the neonatal unit, where she was to spend the next 15 weeks fighting for survival.

Strangely, during that period, I never once thought the worst, not even when we were ushered into a side room while a group of doctors and nurses resuscitated Rhianna and brought her back from the brink. As far as I was concerned, she was in the best hands – more optimism than realism, but certainly something to believe in.

Jane found the whole experience more difficult and was emotionally exhausted as she watched so many other mothers take their babies home, often wondering would this ever even be a possibility for us?

But the nurses were fantastic – you think you have an important job until you spend time in a neonatal ward.

They were a source of great reassurance, always comforting and encouraging. I continued to work, optimistically opting to take paternity leave when Rhianna came home, which meant added pressure on Jane, who was visiting the hospital three times daily.

It was then that TinyLife came into our lives, through the hire of a breast pump, and I learnt all about the great support and services they provide to couples in our situation.

Without going through the experience, it is difficult to understand the value of such help but it is invaluable to those of us who have availed of it.

Thankfully, after 15 long weeks, we were able to take Rhianna home. Her lungs, in particular, were still very delicate and we spent most of the following 12 months indoors, avoiding contact with the general public, until her respiratory system had matured and was able to cope.

And now, here we are, 4 years later with a very healthy, happy, fun loving girl in our lives.

Rhianna is blissfully unaware of her dramatic start in life. We will tell her more about it, as she gets older but, for now, she is our little miracle.

Rhianna Wilton
Born 28 weeks weighing 2lb 8oz

# '*I* learnt about a mother's strength'

Our story does not begin the day that Emily was born but 11 months before, on the day we found out that I was carrying twins. Sadly, at 20 weeks, we were told that I was carrying a rare type of identical twins called mono amniotic twins and they had died in utero.

My boys were born the next day, we named them Nathaniel and Ethan. The next few weeks passed in a blur but our faith, family and friends helped us through those dark days.

My arms felt empty and I longed to fill them. Within 4 months, I was pregnant again but this pregnancy was different. I had lost the innocence I had during the first pregnancy and was frightened of losing this baby too. I was monitored closely throughout the pregnancy due to the small size of the boys.

During a routine check up with the consultant at 31 weeks, it was discovered that my blood pressure had sky rocketed. I was admitted to hospital immediately and following 4 days of treatment, it was decided that the safest thing to do would be to deliver Emily via c-section.

Being told that you are about to deliver a 31 week old baby is truly scary, We got to see Emily for a brief moment before she was sent to neonatal intensive care unit.

I was extremely ill following Emily's birth and could not see her for nearly 24 hours. It was such a long time to be separated from her, I just lay in bed looking at the picture my husband had taken of her, she was so small.

Those first few weeks were very emotional. As I lay in the ward, recovering without my baby beside me, I cried. When I was discharged from hospital, leaving my baby behind, I cried. When I woke up to an alarm at 3am to express milk, without my baby in the moses basket beside me, I cried.

I learnt so much from my experience, in particular that a mother is so much more than her birth story, so much more than someone who brings their newborn home to show off to admirers. I learnt all about a mother's strength, a mother's determination and I quickly learnt that both strength and determination was what I needed to be the best mum I could be for Emily's sake.

Emily came home at 36 weeks gestation and since coming home, she has thrived, even through a few bumps in the road. At 11 months, Emily was admitted to hospital for a blood transfusion due to severe anaemia.

Nowadays, Emily is 19 months and a bundle of energy. Looking at her, you would never know she was born 9 weeks too soon.

I often wonder what it would be like to have a baby born at full term? Emily's early arrival was a difficult time for us but it has taught us to be the parents that we are today.

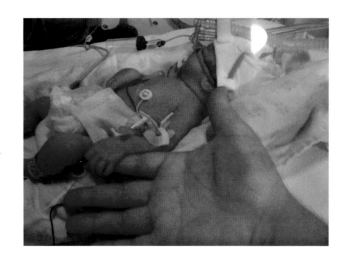

Emily Honan
Born at 31weeks, weighing 3lbs 6oz

# 'Everything happened so fast'

I had had a reasonably easy pregnancy up until I was 29 weeks when I started to bleed. Having gone to the maternity ward of Daisy Hill I was kept in overnight for observations and given injections of steroids for my baby's lungs. I was allowed home the following day (Wednesday) after everything calmed down with the instructions that if I were to bleed again I was to go straight back in. After that I willed my baby to stay where he was.

However on the Sunday I started to experience back pain and continuously needing to use the toilet. I put it down to a kidney infection with the intentions of seeing my own GP the next day. The back pains continued to get worse and when I started to bleed again in the early hours of Monday we contacted the labour suite and went back to the maternity ward.

Everything happened so quickly after that one minute I was in the maternity ward being examined the next thing I know I'm being rushed to the labour ward having been told that I was fully dilated.

The paediatric team was on standby waiting for my baby to be born. When Haiden arrived it felt like a lifetime before we heard him cry out, it was like hearing a defenceless little kitten but it was a relief to hear him. The doctors worked with Haiden at the side of the room and after briefly seeing him he was taken to the nursery where the doctors continued to work with him. We were frightened not knowing what was happening with our baby.

It was a few hours later when we finally got to see Haiden; he was covered by wires and machines to help him breathe. He looked so helpless. I put my hand into his incubator to touch his tiny little fingers, he gripped my finger in his, up until then it hadn't felt real, but my son was here and he was fighting for his life.

That first night away from him was terrible. Even though I was in a room of my own I could still hear all the newborn babies around me, I kept imaging I could hear the machines that were monitoring my baby. I was alone and frightened, it felt like the longest night ever.

The staff in the special care baby unit were wonderful; they talked us through everything that was happening with Haiden. They were there not only for Haiden but also for myself and my husband. They were our family.

I had always wanted to breastfeed my baby but thought it would not be possible due to him being so premature, but still wanted to give him the best possible start in life. The nurses talked to me about expressing milk and it was through them that I learned about TinyLife and their Breast Pump Loan Service. This service meant that I could supply my own milk to Haiden at a time when I could do very little for him.

Haiden thrived daily, tolerating needles, tests and an infection which knocked him back a few weeks. On Monday 11th April at 6 weeks old weighing 5lb 3oz we were finally allowed to take him home. It was the best feeling ever but also the scariest, we'd taken Haiden from 24 hour nursing care to just ourselves at home.

Haiden continues to thrive and has been back to the baby clinic for his review and to the unit to visit his extended family. They will always hold a special place in our hearts for without them we would not have him.

Haiden O'Hara
Born 30 weeks +4 weighing 3lb10.5 oz

A rose can say
"I love you",
Orchids can enthrall,
But a weed bouquet
in a chubby fist
Yes, that says it all.

~Author Unknown

# Giving birth to a very premature baby is frightening

You just never know what to expect from one day to the next.

I was so afraid of everything and often wondered how someone so small could be strong enough to overcome all of the difficulties she had to face'.

'I learnt to treasure every moment that I spent with my little girl. Although I was so afraid of loving her, I couldn't help but love her from the second I saw her. I quickly realised that Abigail was the most precious gift'.

'Having gone through many of the daily challenges that comes with having a very premature baby, Abigail has taught me to be as strong as she is'.

Abigail Russell-Regan born 27 weeks 1lb 8oz

*We* had many ups and downs … it seemed so unfair that our tiny baby was suffering so much'

I went into premature labour on Friday 18th December 2010 and was immediately transferred to the Royal Jubilee Maternity Hospital in the hope that they may be able to stop my labour. Unfortunately our little girl had other ideas and arrived 13 weeks early – we were petrified.

Calli was taken from the delivery suite straight to the neonatal intensive care unit, thankfully she was breathing on her own and didn't require resuscitation at birth. However she was very small and was easily exhausted, so a decision was made to ventilate her to help with her breathing. At just 1 week old, Calli was moved to Antrim Area Hospital. It was a long and tiring journey for such a tiny baby and we were worried in case it would be too much for her.

Calli had suffered a bleed to the brain at birth and lumbar punctures were carried out to check for infection. The tests came back positive and doctors began to treat Calli for meningitis, she was just 2 weeks old!

Over the next 5 weeks, Calli was subject to many blood transfusions and was also diagnosed with Chronic Lung Disease as a result of her prematurity.

We had many ups and downs over those weeks and it seemed so unfair that our tiny baby was suffering so much in her short life. But Calli made great progress, despite needing oxygen from time to time.

By now, she was alternating between tube and bottle feeds and her weight had crept up to 4lb 15oz. We were hopeful that this would mean she would be coming home soon.

On 20th March 2011, just one day before her due date, we got the wonderful news that Calli was finally well enough to be discharged. We were elated but anxious as we were leaving behind the support and guidance of the nursing staff and managing alone. The next few days and weeks were tough but we managed.

Calli is now 6 months old and is doing extremely well.

Calli Connelly: Born 27 weeks weighing 2lbs 3.5oz

'This has been a true rollercoaster ride and we have learnt to take each day as it comes. There is no doubt that our experience has been challenging to us as a family but it has made us stronger and it has made us appreciate just how lucky we have been with Calli.'

Shea Ormbsy: Born 27+6 weeks weighing 2lb 1oz

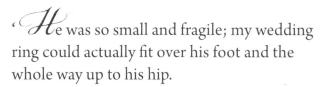

'He was so small and fragile; my wedding ring could actually fit over his foot and the whole way up to his hip.

Yet despite how tiny he was, he just kept fighting.

It is remarkable just how strong these little ones are and how much their little bodies are put through in those first few weeks of life'.

*H*ope is the thing with
feathers that perches
in the soul.

~ Emily Dickenson

'The nurses in charge gave me a Polaroid picture of him. I clung to that picture all night. It was the longest night of my life, all around me were new mothers with their newborn babies crying.

Back home, I remember crying and feeling so angry because life was going on as normal. I felt so guilty doing household chores and at times, I felt bored. After all, I was off on maternity leave and I should have been at home with my baby.

There were very few baby cards in the house and friends and family refused to buy gifts because they were unsure of what the outcome would be'.

Jamie Marshall: Born 27 weeks weighing 1lb 15oz

Sarah Donaghy
Born 32 weeks weighing 3lb 12oz

# 'It wasn't fair'

From the day I found out that I was pregnant, I just knew deep down that something was wrong.

At 24 weeks, I was admitted to hospital with a severe kidney infection. I recalled my initial thoughts and realised that this pregnancy was going to be troublesome.

Just a week later, my waters broke and I was rushed to the Royal Jubilee Maternity Hospital. Everything was happening so fast. I had only just begun to tell people that I was expecting, it was far too soon for the baby to arrive.

As I lay in hospital, I wondered what I had done wrong? I thought I was healthy; I went swimming every day, I tried to eat the right foods, yet here I was on the verge of giving birth and potentially losing my baby. It wasn't fair.

Although my waters had broken, I hadn't gone into labour. Despite this, the nurses had told me to have names ready for the imminent arrival.

After 18 hours in the delivery suite, I was moved to the antenatal ward for the remainder of my pregnancy, however long that would be.

I spent the next 6 weeks in hospital, I was scanned every other day to make sure the baby wasn't suffering any undue stress.

The nurses took me to visit the neonatal unit, just to prepare me for what might lie ahead.

At 32 weeks, an infection meant that the baby was suffering trauma and it was decided that she should be delivered. Following a 36 hour labour and then an emergency section, Sarah was born. She was taken straight to the neonatal unit.

There were so many thoughts running through my head; was she alive, would she be ok? My maternal instinct had taken hold. All I wanted to do was to hold my baby and that had been taken away from me.

Due to her early arrival, Sarah's lungs had not fully developed and she was therefore ventilated. She was so tiny and her skin was transparent.

I felt so helpless as I watched the doctors and nurses working on her. Those first weeks were the hardest and we almost lost her a few times.

Thankfully, TinyLife were on hand to offer me practical support.

I never knew that such a fantastic support network existed. Their help continued for the duration of Sarah's hospital stay. They provided me with a breast pump, information and general help and support. On the day that Sarah was discharged from hospital, she was a tiny 4lb 1oz. It was such a relief to finally have her home.

I was anxious in the first few months and admittedly, we did struggle. Thankfully things did get easier and Sarah began to thrive.

'Premature delivery was something that happened to someone else, not me, the midwife'.

Our son Joel was born at 26 weeks and 4 days gestation, weighing just 840g.

It was an incredible shock for us as my previous pregnancy had been normal and free from complications.

Placenta Praevia and premature delivery was something that happened to someone else, not me, the midwife....or so I thought!

We will never forgot the first time we saw Joel, he looked so tiny in this massive incubator with many leads and monitors attached to every inch of him.  He was the tiniest baby in the neonatal unit.

We felt so helpless watching him fight for his little life it was at that moment I knew what all of those mothers, I provided care for, of preterm babies went through.

The neonatal staff were excellent; they supported and encouraged us throughout those seventeen long, tiresome weeks and we had many highs and lows along the way!

Joel Stevenson
Born 26+4 weeks weighing 840g

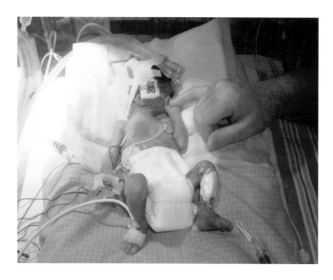

Ready

for the

Rain

# '*I* wished I could put her back where she belonged for the next 13 weeks'.

At 27 weeks, I had placental abruption.

After being rushed to hospital I feared for the worst. I was immediately prepared for an emergency caesarean section. My daughter Brooke, was born and taken immediately to the neonatal unit. I thought this was routine, so that they could check her over and she would be brought back to me. This couldn't have been further from the truth!

I didn't know anything about premature babies, I didn't even know anyone who had a premature baby! Naively, I thought 'they just needed to sleep and grow bigger'. But when I saw Brooke for the first time, I knew my initial thoughts had been very, very wrong!

Brooke had a few setbacks throughout her care but yet, she continued to fight. I, on the other hand, felt incredibly guilty. I wanted to shield my baby from all of the needles and tubes and I longed for the day that she would realise that her life would not be full of pain.

I was completely lost. I couldn't hold her, kiss her, even comfort her when she cried. A lovely nurse helped me to express breast milk, telling me that it was like 'liquid gold' for my baby. At last, I felt I could do something for Brooke, I could finally be her mummy.

Brooke is now a fun loving, 3 year old. We know, we are extremely lucky and blessed.

Brooke Singleton: Born 27 weeks
Weighing 2lb 8oz

Joshua Wallace
Born 29 weeks, weighing 775g

# 'Doctors prepared us for the worst.'

Throughout my pregnancy, I had been very ill but never did we imagine that we would have such a premature baby.

We were so excited to be going for our 29 week scan. The scan was booked for 11.30am but as soon as the doctor began, we noticed she looked very worried. She explained to us that she wanted a second opinion. As soon as the consultant saw the scan, he told us that they would deliver right away.

I had developed pre-eclampsia and the baby had stopped growing at 23 weeks.
I felt numb as I was prepared for surgery, I never imagined something like this would happen to us.

Joshua was born at 2.30pm, just 3 hours after our scan. He weighed just 775g and was immediately rushed to the neonatal intensive care unit.

It felt like a lifetime before we were able to see Joshua and it was scary watching his tiny helpless body attached to lots of wires and beeping monitors.

The doctors prepared us for the worst and we were told that the next 72 hours were critical.

The first few weeks were like a rollercoaster; every day bringing a new challenge.

Joshua developed a bleed in his brain and an infection in his stomach which meant he couldn't start feeding. He had regular brain scans to monitor the bleed and was given strong antibiotics to fight the stomach infection. Just a few weeks later, Joshua was taking half a millilitre of milk.

Some weeks later, doctors discovered that his little body wasn't able to make enough red blood cells and he was given 3 blood transfusions within a very short space of time. But this really helped him and gave him the boost that he needed.

Things were going great until several weeks later, Joshua was rushed to the Royal for a bilateral hernia operation. It felt like such a setback; he'd been doing so well. During the operation, he had taken a bad reaction to the anaesthetic and was put back into intensive care.

Joshua was finally discharged following 10 long weeks in neonatal care. Although he has had many ups and downs during the first few months of his life, he has done amazingly well and we are so proud of him.

'I remember the first time I saw my daughter following her birth, she was perfect, miniature, like a doll.'

In fact, when Hannah was finally moved into her first hospital cot, I couldn't get clothes that were small enough to fit her so I went to our local toy shop and bought her dolls clothes'.

'When Hannah was finally discharged, all of my initial worries were still there, would she walk, would she talk and run? All the things normal children do?

The answer is- she can do everything. She never ceased to amaze me as she overcame every obstacle'.

Hannah Hillis; Born 24 weeks weighing 1lb 10oz

'*I* felt so helpless, I could do nothing for my twins, it was all out of my hands.'

Alexandra 2lb 12oz:Amber 2lb 14oz Born 29 weeks

$\mathcal{T}$here are only two
lasting bequests that we
can hope to give to our
children. One is roots,
the other wings.

~Carter Hodding

'*Premature babies, even those who are lost, provide us with hope in so many ways.*'

Our daughter Megan was born on 25th September 2007 at 26 weeks gestation, she was the smallest baby in Northern Ireland at the time, weighing just 1lb 2.5oz. Megan was delivered early as a result of pre-eclampsia, the disease being so sudden and severe that it is life-threatening to both mother and baby.

Megan fought so hard to overcome many obstacles, and had to endure 3 operations as a direct result of her prematurity. She made wonderful progress, but also suffered many setbacks, and was hospitalised for 3 months in the neonatal intensive care unit before being moved to the special care baby unit.

While there, my husband and I experienced some terrible tragedies but also met some of the kindest and most dedicated people imaginable. We made friends for life.

Sadly, Megan lost her battle for life in March 2008; it was so hard to see a future without her. We wanted to create a lasting legacy in her name and went on to raise in the region of £15,000 for TinyLife by organising 'Megan's Walk', a walk from the Royal Victoria Hospital to Craigavon Area Hospital, to trace Megan's journey. Public generosity and sympathy for Megan's plight was amazing and it helped get us through those early days.

In March 2009, on the anniversary of Megan's death, I found out I was expecting again. We were over the moon but so anxious, however my medical care from the outset of the pregnancy was extremely attentive and at 38 weeks gestation, we were introduced to Charlie – a healthy baby son, born with Megan's feisty spirit.

We have always felt that Megan has been beside us since she was released from her pain, and Charlie is special in so many ways. He is so similar to her in looks and in character and we feel so lucky to have him.

Premature babies, even those who are lost, provide us with hope in so many ways. Megan has changed our lives completely, and lives on through her little brother Charlie, a healthy and happy boy who helps to heal our hearts a little bit more every day.

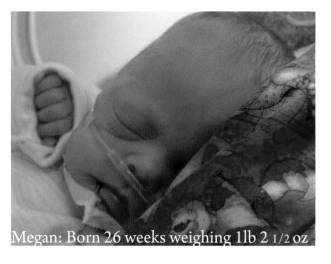

Megan: Born 26 weeks weighing 1lb 2 1/2 oz

Charlie White: Born 38weeks weighing 7lb 9oz

I brought children
into this dark world
because it needed the light
that only a child can bring.


~Liz Armbruster

$\mathcal{W}$hen you think everything is lost, just remember, that miracles do happen

Our little girl is here to prove that'.

Rebekah Dalzell- McGhee: Born 31 weeks, weighing 2lbs 13oz

Saul Wilton
Born 34 weeks weighing 4lbs1oz

'I have learnt that a mother's instinct is a powerful tool in the care of a child with complex medical needs'.

'One nurse described expressed milk as 'liquid gold' for premature and sick babies and I expressed for Saul for nine months. It was one of the few yet most important things I could do for him in those early days'.

'I felt like I had let him down by not being able to keep him inside me until his due date'.

Lewis Davison: Born 31 weeks, weighing 3lb 4oz

*Tiny Tales of Hope*

# Would my baby even survive?'

All had been going well throughout my pregnancy, until one day I noticed my feet and ankles were a bit swollen. I was 32 weeks pregnant and knew that it was common for women's feet to swell in later pregnancy.

I was absolutely astounded to find out that not only did I have pre-eclampsia but the highest blood pressure my doctor had ever seen in a pregnant woman!

The doctor explained to me the dangers of the condition and said that the baby would be delivered earlier than expected. Naively, I thought he meant in a few more weeks but I was shocked when he told me to prepare for delivery in the morning.

My thoughts spiralled, I hadn't even bought a pram, let alone a bag for the hospital! I was petrified for my baby coming 8 weeks early – all I could think was, would the baby survive?

I was given steroid injections to help strengthen the baby's lungs and I was prepared for delivery. I remember the doctor saying that it was a good sign if the baby cried when it was born. We were overjoyed to hear Lucy's tiny cry as she entered the world, all 3lb 14oz of her.

Lucy was quickly taken to the neonatal unit to be ventilated. I remember the first time I saw her; this tiny little body, wired up to tubes and monitors, with a giant oxygen mask on her face. It was frightening but I knew, deep down, that she was in the best place.

Luckily, Lucy spent just one night in the intensive care unit before being transferred to the main unit. Yet, she still had to be tube fed as at 32 weeks her sucking reflex hadn't yet developed.

We visited Lucy every single day but I longed to take her home, and I hated having to get to know my baby in such a public environment, we just wanted some private time with her, to be a little family.

The day we were told we could take her home was momentous. But we were so scared! How would we look after this tiny, premature baby all by ourselves?

Thankfully, Lucy was one of the lucky ones. It all happened so fast that we really didn't have time to think about what was going on. Looking back, this was a blessing.

One thing I have learnt is that there is light at the end of the tunnel, no matter how long that tunnel might be. We have since had a second baby, Lila, with no complications which shows that just because you have one premature baby, certainly doesn't mean that you will have another. And there are happy endings out there, I am so thankful we had one of them!

Lucy Hyde: Born 32 weeks weighing 3lb 14oz

'My pregnancy was straight-forward at the beginning and at our 22 week scan, everything was normal and on track. We began to look forward to our new arrival'.

At my 25 week appointment with the mid-wife, my blood pressure was extremely high with 4 pluses of protein in my urine. Immediately, I was sent to hospital to be monitored. After being assessed, the doctor told me that I had severe pre-eclampsia. They gave me steroids to mature the baby's lungs then sent me straight to the delivery ward where I was started on magnesium sulphate to try to stablise my blood pressure.

Within hours, I was being transferred to the Royal Jubilee Maternity Hospital. On arrival, I was swabbed for Swine Flu. The results came back positive; I was isolated and began treatment.

The doctor informed us that they had no choice but to deliver Callum as this was the only way I would recover.

Over the next few days, my blood pressure became stabilised until I developed severe pain below my ribs and blood tests indicated that I had developed HELLP syndrome, which is a severe complication of pre-eclampsia which affects the body's blood clotting and liver functions.

At 17.33pm, Callum was born via emergency caesarean section, he measured just 6 inches from head to toe but thankfully he showed signs of life; crying twice and breathing on his own.

The doctors worked with Callum in the theatre for a short period, giving my husband Shane the chance to have a quick look at him then once Callum was stable enough, they whisked him straight to the neonatal intensive care unit.

A consultant paediatrician came to meet with us and explained that whilst Callum was stable, he was a lot smaller than they had anticipated so his chance of survival was extremely small. We were told to be realistic and take things an hour at a time.

We were devastated to think of our little boy, fighting for his life and what hurt us more was to think that we could do nothing for him.

Some hours later, we were allowed to see Callum. It was terrifying, he was connected to a high frequency ventilator and there were wires with machines everywhere. He was extremely tiny and his skin was transparent.

Over the next few days, Callum remained stable, receiving little oxygen on the ventilator. We were really surprised to see just how well he was coping. But we were warned that most premature babies have a 'settling in' period and we were told to continue to expect the worst over the coming weeks.

On Christmas day, Callum was a week old. When we arrived at the hospital that morning, there was a present from TinyLife including our first card from Callum and a vest, teddy and blanket. It was such a wonderful thought on what was always going to be one of the hardest days of our journey so far. It was the first time we got to touch our baby boy and we finally got to change his tiny nappy.

The next few months were like a rollercoaster, one minute we would watch Callum grow stronger, then the next minute he would be battling infections. Callum received a total of 11 blood transfusions, surgery to correct 2 hernias and surgery on both eyes to prevent retinal detachment which could result in blindness. We watched on as he defied all odds.

After almost 8 weeks, Callum was transferred to Craigavon neonatal unit where he continued to thrive. On 29th March 2011 (Callum's actual due date), after 101 days in Neonatal, we finally got to bring our precious son home weighing 4lb 7oz; it was a truly magical day for everyone, including family and friends as many of them had only seen photographs of Callum .

Having a premature baby is an immensely terrifying ordeal. You learn to live a day at a time and every day you thank God that your baby is growing a little stronger. Yet somehow you find the strength to carry on. You form bonds with nurses and doctors, people you thought you would never end up depending on so much.

We came to realise that we owed our sons survival to these people. During our experience, we were constantly reminded that 'where there is life, there is hope' and that will always stick with us.

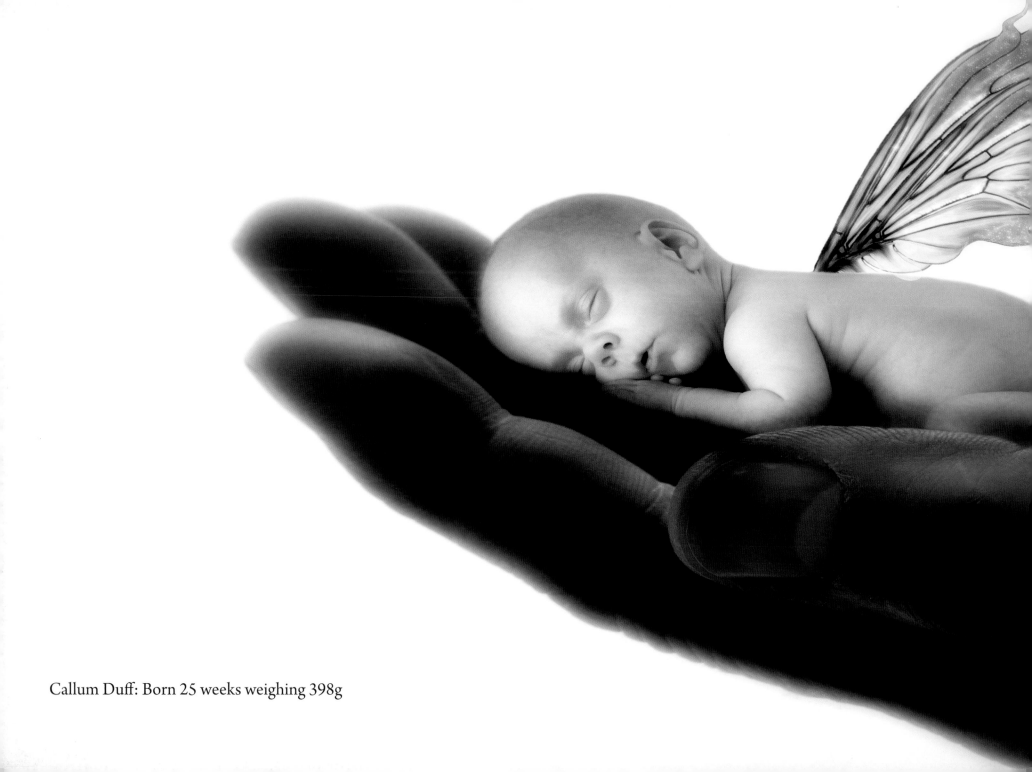

Callum Duff: Born 25 weeks weighing 398g

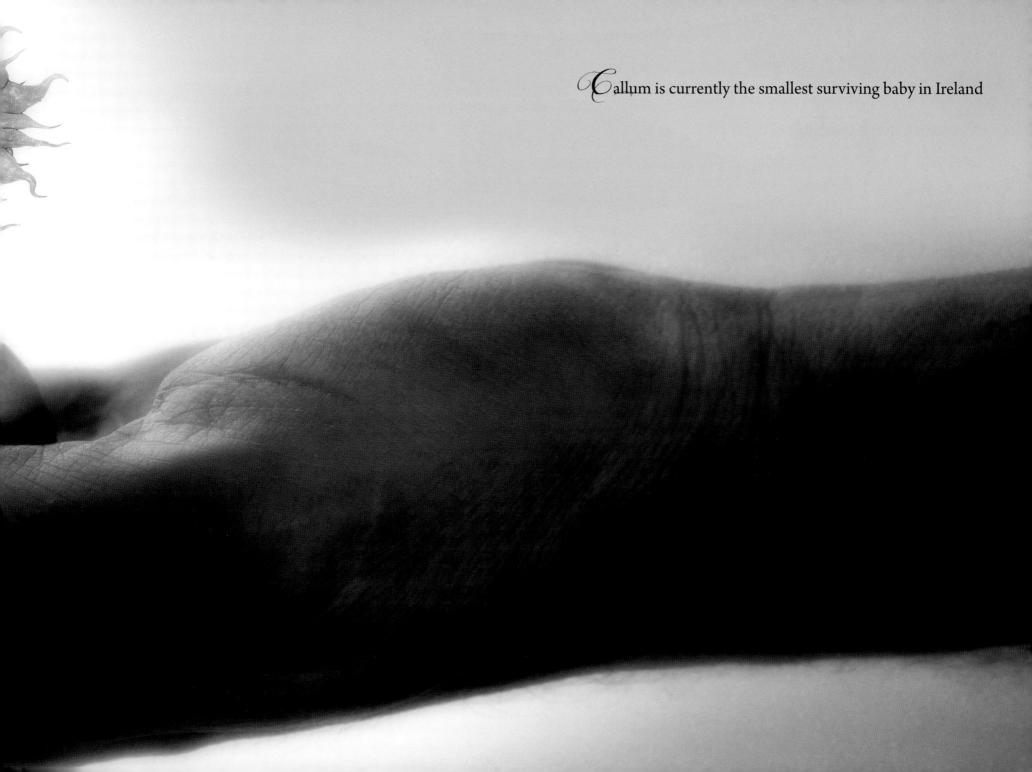

Callum is currently the smallest surviving baby in Ireland

# 'The hardest part was knowing that they hadn't felt my touch or been held in my arms.'

The evening before I was due to give birth, a neonatal nurse came to see me to explain how premature babies are cared for in the neonatal unit.

In hindsight, this was probably the most worthwhile chat I could have had as no one realises the emotional attachment a mother feels for her babies from the moment they are born.

There they were, these two little mites, covered in wires, tubes down their throats and noises from monitors beeping constantly. The hardest part was knowing that they hadn't felt my touch or been held in my arms.

To make it worse, I had to return to a post-natal ward, full of other mums who were dealing excitedly with their newborns and visitors. We didn't really have any visitors apart from immediate family, as there were no babies to see or visit.

Adam and Ben McMaster: Born 34 weeks. Adam 5lb 10oz Ben 4lb 11oz

# '*Just* when you think things are going great a new infection hits...'

Being the parents of a premature baby isn't something you plan.

Our eldest daughter, Dia was born at 28 weeks, weighing 2lb 15oz. She spent 11 weeks in the neonatal unit in Craigavon Area Hospital.

Having been through the ordeal of premature birth once, you would think that Shane and I would be able to cope with it again when Cala made her dramatic entrance into the world at 30 weeks. But this couldn't be further from the truth!

You can never truly be prepared for that rollercoaster of emotions. You watch your baby every day for weeks, even months, struggling to find health, strength and the will to keep fighting.

There are so many things that parents of full term babies take for granted; simple things like changing a nappy that we had to wait weeks to experience.

We learnt a whole new language, words we never expected to hear – respiratory distress syndrome, apnoea, bleeding on the brain, pneumonia and the list went on. And just when you think that things are going great, a new infection hits.

You long for the day to bring your baby home, so you can be a 'normal' family but nothing is 'normal' for the parents of a premature baby. Your days are filled with hospital appointments, check ups, assessments, infection control.

But no matter how bad it got, TinyLife were always there; they lent us a breast pump and offered great practical advice, as well as a listening ear.

Today, Dia is 6 and Cala almost 3; we look at them and often remember everything they have been through. They really are 'our little miracles of hope.

Dia McCrory: Born 28 weeks weighing 2lb 15oz

Cala McCrory: Born 30 weeks weighing 3lbs 5oz

*Tiny Tales of Hope*

Jamie 2lb 5oz and Scott Hood 2lb 9oz: Born 27 weeks

# '*I* couldn't bear to bury any more children'

We were only married a few months when we lost our first baby at 11 weeks and we were devastated. The following year we lost our second baby at 7 weeks.

The next year, we were extremely excited to be told that we were expecting twins but I went into premature labour and at 19 weeks, our baby son Jack was born asleep, three weeks later at nearly 22 weeks, our second son, Joshua was born. Joshua only lived for 2 hours which gave us time as a mummy and daddy to tell him all the things we would never get the chance to say. We fitted a life-time of love into those few precious hours. Joshua passed away peacefully in my arms.

We said goodbye to our beautiful sons and buried them together in the church graveyard where we had been married. It was the hardest day of our life.

Just a year later, we found out that I was preg-nant again with twins but at 22 weeks tragedy struck, I was in premature labour again.

I begging the doctors to save our babies, I couldn't bear to bury any more children.

Fortunately the hospital were able to stop my labour until 27 weeks when further complications set in and I had to have an emergency 'c' section to save both the babies and me. On 15th December 2006, I became a mummy again to Scott and Jamie, weighing 2lb 9oz and 2lb 5oz respectively.

They were immediately put into incubators and taken to the Royal Jubilee Special Care Baby Unit. Seeing our babies for the first time was frightening; they were so small, so fragile and we were told to prepare for the worst. On Christmas Eve, just 10 days after their early arrival, both boys had to have the first of many blood transfusions.

Having a premature baby is an uphill struggle and in our case, the struggle was multiplied by two. It changes your life forever.

The boys had numerous medical conditions, Scott had a secondary bleed in the left ven-tricle of his brain and had to endure frequent MRI scans, he had reflux of both kidneys,

a slight heart murmur and he required an operation, at just 9 wks, to reposition his appendix.

Jamie had a severe heart murmur which needed to be treated immediately, an umbilical hernia and later developed reflux.

Every single day was a challenge, we watched helplessly as our tiny babies, fought for their lives.

After a month, the boys were transferred to Craigavon Area Hospital. It was a huge mile-stone for us all. We were waiting for the MRI results to indicate if there were symptoms of cerebral palsy. We felt so alone; parenthood was not the way we had imagined it would be. We were not able to hold our babies or show them how much we loved them. We watched helplessly as the wonderful nurses did every-thing for them, whilst we could do nothing.

After a total of 78 days in hospital, we were finally able to bring our boys home and begin life as a proper family.

The boys are now happy, healthy 4 years olds and they started P1 in September.

'They say the euphoria of becoming parents is wasted on those who have premature babies, and they couldn't be more right!'

'She had a lumbar puncture test done for meningitis and suddenly our world was falling apart...'

'The hardest part, was to think that Erin had to fight all on her own accord; no one could do the fighting for her'.

Erin Daly: born 26 weeks weighing 2lb 1oz

When my waters broke 10 weeks early, I was shocked – I hadn't attended an antenatal class or even heard of a neonatal unit!'

'I was fortunate enough to avail of one of the TinyLife breast pumps. Being able to express milk for Sam made me feel like I was doing something beneficial for him'.

Sam Geary: born 30 weeks weighing 3lb 3oz

*Tiny Tales of Hope*

# 'At 30 weeks, we had very little prepared'

As a first time mum, I had no idea that your waters could 'leak', so when I felt a 'trickling sensation' at just 30 weeks, I didn't realise that this was my waters breaking. Naively, I just thought they would burst and the labour pains would closely follow.

To be sure, I called my midwife who told me to come to the hospital immediately. When I arrived, they scanned me and tested the fluid to check if it was indeed amniotic fluid. They confirmed that it was amniotic fluid but explained that it was still possible for me to reach full term but the likelihood would be that the baby would arrive early.

To be safe, they administered 2 steriod injections to strengthen the baby's lungs and transferred me to the Royal Jubilee Maternity Hospital ,who were better equipped at dealing with preterm infants.

Two days after being admitted and without any signs of labour, I was taken for an ultrasound scan so they could assess how much fluid was around the baby. It was at that moment I decided to find out the sex of the baby.

At 30 weeks, we had very little prepared, so I reasoned that if we found out and I did go into early labour then my husband James could go out and get everything we needed.

It's funny because no matter how much you are prepared for premature birth, there is always a little anxiety about what might lie ahead. Based on this, we decided to name the baby so that she would have a name from the moment she arrived.

As the day progressed, I began to feel ill then that evening my contractions started. I was closely monitored as they were concerned that with the waters gone, both the baby and I would be at risk of infection. It was decided that an emergency section would be the best type of delivery and so, on 19th February, nearly 10 weeks before her due date, Ruby was born.

Ruby was taken to the neonatal unit to learn how to feed and to grow stronger. Looking around the unit, there were so many sick babies, we felt so lucky that Ruby was well in comparison. Luckily, after just 3 weeks, Ruby was transferred to the Ulster Hospital Dundonald.

After a week, we were given the news that Ruby could come home, she was a tiny 4lb 12oz. Finally having her at home was fantastic. It meant that family and friends could meet our little girl.

People have always commented on how scared we must have been at the time but I can honestly say that the people we have encountered due to Ruby's prematurity were wonderful. They were reassuring and encouraging which meant we never felt alone.

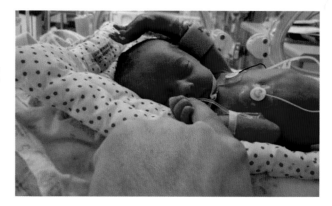

Ruby McKernan: Born 30 weeks weighing 3lb 5oz

There is no medicine
like hope.
No incentive so great,
and no tonic so powerful.

~Orison Swett Marden

'The baby was not due for over three months; Anita was just beginning to show, nothing had been bought, antenatal classes had not yet begun. We didn't even have time to think about the seriousness of what was happening'

Alexandra Hogg born 28 weeks weighing 2lb 3oz

India Hanna 1lb 8oz, Khloe Hanna 1lb 11oz
Olly Hanna 1lb 7oz. Born 25+2 weeks

Sadly, Olly passed away peacefully at 12 days old. The little blue teddy bear symbolises that he will always be with his sisters.

# 'We spent Christmas Day, willing our baby to live'

We didn't expect the last few months of my second pregnancy to be so dramatic. In fact, our baby wasn't due until the end of January and we were looking forward to spending Christmas with our toddler, Joshua.

Unexpectedly, at 29 weeks, I was rushed into hospital and after 3 weeks complete bed rest, baby Oliver arrived weighing just 5lb 1oz. Oliver was so tiny and was quickly whisked away to the special care unit. Going back to my room with no baby was awful, I felt so empty.

It was heartbreaking for us to see our tiny baby covered in wires and tubes. He was extremely ill with E Coli Septicaemia and he was so fragile, we were afraid to even touch him!

Fear gripped us when we were then told that Oliver needed a lumbar puncture to determine if he had meningitis. It wasn't right that this tiny baby was being subjected to such an invasive and painful procedure.

Leaving hospital without him was heart-breaking but he needed further treatment and we had a toddler at home who desperately needed his mummy too. I felt torn apart, like I wasn't doing a good enough job for either of my two children, but looking back now, I know I did what was best!

As Christmas drew closer, travelling up and down to hospital three times a day was quite surreal. Everywhere we looked, people were preparing for the festive season and all we wanted to do was cancel Christmas. We tried to keep things as normal as possible for Joshua.

We spent Christmas morning at home with Joshua but it was hard for our little boy to understand why mummy and daddy needed to go back to hospital.

After spending the first 23 days of his little life in an incubator, Oliver was finally discharged. What a wonderful feeling to be finally introducing Oliver to his big brother.

Naturally, we had to be careful of infections and we have had some minor setbacks along the way but this December, Oliver will be celebrating his 3rd birthday as well as his first Christmas as big brother to our new addition, baby Georgia.

Every Christmas, we think of the parents with premature babies in hospital, who are asking themselves, as we did, 'When will it be our turn to bring our baby home'.

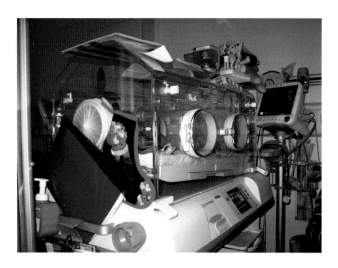

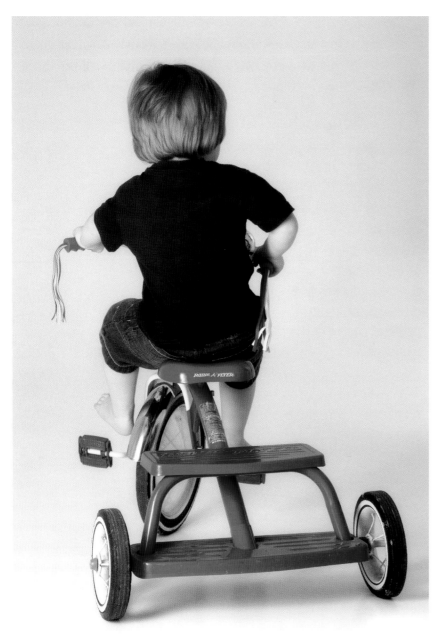

Oliver Maw born 33 weeks weighing 5lb 1oz

Ben and Alexander Magee
Born 33 weeks
Ben weighing 2lb15oz
Alexander weighing 4lb 3oz

# 'I think there is another one in there'.

After 8 years of trying to conceive, my husband and I were told that IVF was our only option. It was a step I didn't want us to take, for me, the chapter was closed.

A few weeks later, I was utterly astounded to find out I was pregnant and at my first scan, we were shocked when the consultant said, 'I think there is another one in there'!

Our boys arrived 7 weeks early and spent several days in the Royal Jubilee Hospital before being transferred to the Ulster Hospital Dundonald, for a further 2 weeks. At times, it was daunting and emotional, especially seeing your babies, lying there so helpless, covered in wires and being tube fed but the neonatal staff were wonderfully supportive and very encouraging.

We were very lucky when both boys were discharged together and that is when the fun really started. To say we were busy was an understatement. I was so grateful for any visitors, especially at feeding and bath time.

I had heard of TinyLife when I was pregnant so I decided to go along to their Parents Support Group. It was a decision that changed my life. I began to look forward to meeting other parents of twins and premature babies; it was wonderful to know that other people were experiencing the same joys, difficulties and challenges as us.

At the first group, I found out about the Family Support Services that TinyLife provides to families of premature and sick babies. I thought it would be wonderful to have some help once a week and TinyLife matched me with a perfect volunteer. Finally, we were able to take the boys to swimming and baby yoga; things I would have found impossible to manage by myself.

At the boys' Baptism and first birthday, we asked friends and family to donate to TinyLife rather than buying presents; we just wanted to express our gratitude for all their support. We will continue to be involved with TinyLife, it is such a fantastic charity and provides a lifeline to families like us.

# 'This tiny little life gave us so much hope'

From the early stages of my pregnancy, I had had some problems. At 19 weeks, I began to bleed heavily and we went to A & E, expecting to have miscarried. To our amazement, the baby was still there with a strong heartbeat – we were so thankful.

The doctors advised me that the best course of action would be bed rest and it was decided that I would stay in hospital until the baby was delivered.

At just 25 weeks, I was transferred to the Royal Jubilee Maternity Hospital to deliver the baby. Aimee was born at 25+1 weeks, weighing just 760g. She was gravely ill and we were told to expect the worst.

The next few weeks were filled with ups and downs. We took every day as it came and tried to focus on the day we would be going home as a family. She was so tiny and helpless but the love we felt for her was unimaginable, despite our circumstances.

It often felt like we were living a nightmare. We found it so hard to imagine that this tiny little life in front of us could be so strong and as we saw her little personality develop in those early days in the hospital it gave us so much hope.

We quickly realised that Aimee was one of the many, many special children out there, who survived against all odds.

Aimee is now 3 years old and has not suffered any long term effects due to her prematurity. She is our little miracle.

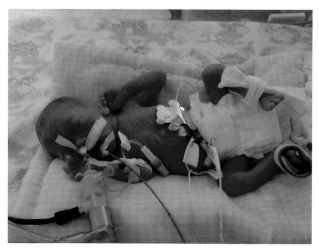

Aimee Elder
Born 25+1 weeks, weighing 760g

72

A smile from a baby
is a curve that sets
everything straight.

~Anonymous

We were devastated, as we were finally coming to terms with the fact that our baby was here, almost 15 weeks early, he had fought so hard to survive and now he could be taken from us after such a short time.

I remember the nurse suggested we name him in case something happened. We thought it was a good idea, simply because we couldn't bear to register his birth and death at the same time.

During that time we cried, we prayed and we hoped that he would be strong enough to make it and thankfully he was.

Rhys was 107 days old when he was finally discharged from hospital'.

Rhys Lockhart  born 25 weeks weighing 2lb 2oz

David-Ross Richardson Born 23+5 weeks weighing 1lb 7oz

'For any mums and dads today who have had a premature baby, take comfort in knowing that although your world has been turned upside down, there is always hope and that is what will get you through the hard times'.

$\mathcal{B}$ringing Harry home was fantastic yet very daunting. He was only 2lb 2oz so he was still vulnerable to infection, he was also on a strict 4 hourly feeding schedule.

Whilst he was in hospital, he wasn't allowed any visitors other than us, so the best part of his homecoming was that it meant he could finally meet his big sister, grandparents and the extended family'.

Harry Grain Born 30 weeks weighing 2lb 2oz

*B*arry McManamon
Born 29 weeks weighing 3lb 4oz

Eden Smith: Born 28 weeks weighing 2lb 3 oz

The doctors decided that the baby would have a better chance of survival outside the womb'.

We also had two sons at home, Brogan was 7 years old and Carthach just 4. They knew all about their baby sisters but because of the increased risk of infection, we couldn't bring the boys to the hospital to meet them'.

Eabha  Mulholland 1lb 14oz, Frea Mulholland 2lb: Born 27 weeks

# 'We had to just accept that our baby was coming early'

We were so excited to find out that we were expecting our first baby.

Our due date was 12th February 2010 and like every expectant parent, we aimed for that day. So when I went into labour, 6 weeks early, it was a big shock.

On New Years Eve, I attended the hospital because of heavy discharge and was told I had possible Strep B and was given a leaflet to read. Luckily for me, I read the leaflet wrong and thought it said I'd probably go into labour at 37 weeks, however, my husband read it correctly and it said that I wouldn't even make 37 weeks!

So on 4th January, I went back to work after the Christmas break and by 10am, I had started to bleed. After calling my midwife, I decided to go and get it checked out. I didn't even log off my computer because I assumed I would be back later that day. Little did I know this was the start of my labour!

The hospital attempted to stop my labour progressing but it was too late. We had to just accept that our baby was coming. I was given antibiotics on a drip for Strep B to prevent it from being passed to the baby and also steroid injections to help the baby's lungs in case they weren't fully developed.

The following afternoon, our beautiful baby boy was born via ventose delivery, we named him Evan. He weighed just 4lb 4oz and he was immediately treated by several paediatricians.

The first 24 hours were nerve racking. Luckily he was able to feed and breathe on his own but feeding time in particular was quite difficult as he had to be fed every 3 hours, often he wouldn't even be able to manage 1oz.

Bringing him home for the first time was very exciting but also frightening. It was the heart of January, the snow was lying thick on the ground and we had this little bundle of joy, dressed in clothes that were far too big on him and sitting in a huge car seat.

Those first few weeks were so nerve racking, we felt completely out of our depth and every time he was sick, I was all set for returning to the hospital.

Our biggest milestone was getting to 1 month; after that, Evan came on leaps and bounds and now, people are always amazed to hear that he was 6 weeks premature!

Evan Rees: Born 34 weeks, weighing 4lb 4oz

Such tiny hands to hold
our hearts forever.


~Pam Brown

*H*aving a premature baby is just one of those things you never imagine will happen to you. When it happened to us, our lives changed forever'.

Words cannot describe how it feels to have a baby in neonatal care for a long time. The early days were a bit of a blur for both of us and I often felt like I was visiting someone else's baby. We were humbled by the care and attention given to Evie by everyone in the unit.

Despite Evie's early arrival she is thriving. Her development will continue to be monitored due to having Down's Syndrome. We know that it may take her a little longer to reach her milestones but we have every confidence that she will get there.

Evie Kirk: Born 29+6 weeks weighing 2lb 2oz

*Tiny Tales of Hope*

'I'd had a really easy pregnancy then at my 20 weeks scan it was discovered that I had a low lying placenta.

My consultant explained what would happen if the placenta didn't move, including premature birth. At 33 weeks, I started to bleed and it was decided that the best thing to do would be to deliver baby there and then.

I remember bursting into tears, I wasn't ready to be someone else's Mummy just yet – it was far too early!'

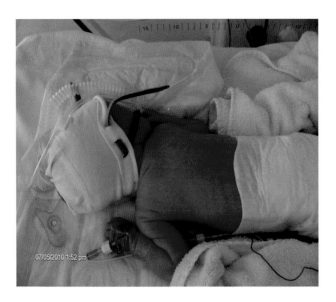

Harley Robinson born 33 weeks weighing 4lb 5 1/2 oz

*Tiny Tales of Hope*

*A* new baby is like the
beginning of all things-
wonder, hope, a dream
of possibilities.

~Eda Leshan

Helen Boyd 1lb13oz: Megan Boyd 2lb1/2oz. Born 26 weeks

Jonathan Hill: Born 29 weeks weighing 3lb 2 1/2 oz

'At this stage of my pregnancy, we hadn't even thought about names yet. But the nurses recommended we named him. I remember we both looked at each other and said 'Jonathan' which meant, 'Gift from God'. It was so true, he really was our gift from God'.

'The doctor gently told us that the survival rate for babies born at 27 weeks was 50/50. The weeks that followed their early arrival were filled with highs and lows. Both boys needed various blood transfusions, their tiny veins collapsed resulting in drips and needles being attached through their heads. Yet with every hurdle, they fought and pulled through.

They are now 19 years old, Jamie is a professional jockey and Jason has completed his A'Levels and is hoping to go to university'.

Jamie Sloan 1lb 12oz  Jason Sloan 2lb 4oz: Born 27 weeks

# 'I couldn't cope with how fragile she seemed'

Hannah was born on the 12th of June at exactly 26 weeks. I began to suffer pains in my back during the weekend before but believed it was maybe a kidney infection. I am a teacher and went to school as normal on the Monday thinking the pain would surely pass.

I had a little boy of 14 months and my husband was working in Scotland at the time. The pain was still there on the Tuesday morning and I thought I should go to the hospital to put my mind at rest. I drove myself to the hospital along with my little boy thinking I could then go onto school afterwards.

However, at the hospital I was told the baby was about to be born! I lay in the delivery suite from Tuesday morning until Thursday evening when Hannah was born. I wasn't in pain the whole time. The doctors and midwives assured me that the longer Hannah could stay in the womb, the greater her chances were so I just lay very still and prayed that everything would be ok.

I had been told that if she could make it past 26 weeks then that would be even better. Come Thursday evening, Hannah was born.

Hannah survived that night and so began a rollercoaster of events and emotions over the next 3 months which ranged from relief at her birth through to total fear of going into the neonatal unit to see Hannah (I couldn't cope with how fragile she seemed) and then the joy and excitement of her finally getting home from the hospital in September close to her original due date.

There were so many ups and downs before she was able to come home and of course I also had my little boy Matthew to look after. Hannah has just turned 8 years old and thankfully is thriving. She has a terrific personality and is very determined.

It is this aspect of her personality which I know helped her to survive when she was born and I am extremely proud of her.

Hannah Frater: Born 26 weeks weighing 2lb 1/2 oz

Cara, Brogan and Eoin Brackenbury: Born 29 weeks
Cara 2lb 5oz: Brogan 2lb 6oz: Eoin 1lb 11oz

Beth Mooney: Born 35 weeks, weighing 5lb 4oz

Caitlin Mooney: Born 35 weeks, weighing 4lb 8 1/2 oz

'*I* missed that moment when you get to hold your baby in your arms and stare into their eyes for the first time'.

# 'I couldn't allow myself to become attached to Shea, in case something happened'

Our pregnancy with Shea seemed to be going well. I had bled early on and had gained quite a lot of weight but as a first time mum, I didn't really know what to expect. Luckily my aunt and mother are both retired nurses and felt that I should seek some medical advice, just to put my mind at rest. I went along to see my midwife and was told that although I did have traces of protein in my urine, it was probably just a Urinary Tract Infection.

Some weeks later, I began to feel a dull pain in my ribcage. The pain escalated then subsided and I carried on with my usual daily routine. When my husband, Charlie collected me from work that evening, we decided to go to the hospital, to confirm that everything was fine.

The midwife checked the baby's heartbeat, which was perfect and then sent me for a quick scan.

During the scan, the doctor asked me how many weeks pregnant I was, when I answered 25 weeks, she told me that the scanning machine was measuring the baby at just 22 weeks. Suddenly, a consultant was called for a second opinion and once she scanned me it was decided that the baby would be delivered straight away.

Everything passed very quickly in a blur, panic set in as my blood pressure escalated and I was given steroid injections to hasten the baby's lungs for delivery. The Royal Jubilee Maternity Hospital were able to offer a cot in their neonatal unit and I was transferred there immediately.

On arrival at the hospital, we met with a consultant who gently prepared us for the worst. There was a high chance that our baby would not be born alive and if he was, he would probably only survive for a few hours. In order to give our baby the best chance of survival, we opted for a caesarean section.

There were 14 staff members in the theatre that night. Shea came into the world at 9.56pm and was immediately whisked away by a dedicated team of doctors and nurses.

The consultant returned 20 minutes later to tell us that whilst Shea was alive, prognosis was poor as he had been so compromised during the latter stage of my pregnancy and as a result was incredibly small.

It was 24 hours later before I would finally meet Shea for the first time. We were advised that Shea was gravely ill and amongst other complications, he had suffered a grade three bilateral bleed on the brain.

Although we had been prepared for the worst, Charlie was so excited and talked for hours about Shea and our future together as a family. I, on the other hand, did not want to allow myself to become attached to Shea. I referred to him as 'it', even after I was discharged from hospital. It was just how I coped in the early days.

Nevertheless , I knew I had brought this child into the world and he needed a mum, so I began to investigate things I could do to help this little baby survive. The first thing I was advised to do was to express breast milk to feed him and I continued to do this for over 20 weeks.

contd:

Each day brought tears of happiness, tears of joy and often frustration; some days Shea's progress changed hourly. But one thing was for certain, no matter how tired he got, he never gave up his fight and as each day passed, we looked forward and dreamt of the day we could finally take him home.

Just a few days later, we noticed that Shea's stomach was very swollen and it was discovered that his kidneys were not functioning. It was the toughest day to date, we cried a lot and questioned why we had been burdened with this situation. Charlie began to plan a funeral, it was heartbreaking. But at the end of the day, Shea had marginally improved and we left the unit for the night.

I was discharged soon afterwards. It was so difficult walking out of the hospital without my baby. It felt like I was abandoning him. Shea continued to make slow progress; we had more bad days than good days as he battled on.

We had many meetings with his consultant, who would be frank about his prognosis. I was petrified of what the future would hold for us all; suddenly it became clear to me that I wasn't going to have my 'perfect' child and I wondered how we would cope with a child who had complex needs.

Shea continued to make process with varying degrees of success, although some days he was very ill. Our journey up until this stage was very physically and emotionally draining. We were never sure what each new day would bring and we were always uncertain of what the future would hold for us.

We relied heavily on each other and the other parents in the unit because they were the only people who knew how we were feeling and what we were going through.

One day we arrived at the hospital and there was a lot of activity in the nursery. Apparently a dangerous infection had broken out and a number of babies had been moved to isolation. Shea was one of those babies and he remained in isolation until his discharge some 3 months later.

As Shea grew stronger, the doctors and nurses encouraged us to bring his pram to the hospital and take him out for short walks around the grounds. It was nerve racking at first but it was fantastic to have some normality in our lives.

Eventually, on 15th August, we got the wonderful news that Shea was to be discharged. It was a fantastic feeling to walk out of the hospital but we were also aware that we were leaving behind our support network who were on call 24/7 to offer advice and medical assistance.

Shea still had many appointments with the hospital following discharge to monitor his progress. At one appointment, the doctor realised that Shea was struggling to focus and he was referred to an eye consultant for laser eye treatment. Shea was diagnosed with Retinopathy of Prematurity and he is consequently registered blind.

He has had a number of surgeries including hernia operations, eye surgeries and a PEG placed in situ. Thankfully he was discharged from Cardiology when he was 2 years old as the cardiac duct had closed without the need for surgery. He has come through so much in his short life time and he has developed a very high pain threshold.

After each operation, Shea has battled on and has grown into a very happy and sociable little boy.

He came before his time
A child so small and yet sublime
Heartbeat thumping, pitter pat,
Wondering how and where it's at,
Precious music to our ears
Hands to hold and still the fears.

Gentle footsteps in the night,
Treasured hopes forever bright.
Brightest being, gift from high,
Gentlest, sweetest, lullaby.

Marvel at his perfect feet,
Born of precious single beat.
Singing joyful little song,
Our hearts to yours will now belong.

This final bond to tie so sure,
Completes a love so strong and pure.
Now whisper softly, while he's asleep,
His life and future ours to keep.

~

By Pat McErlean (Shea's Grandfather, 2009)

Shea Simpson Born 25+4 weeks weighing 506g

Dedicated to my mum and dad who
always believe in everything I do.
Without your support and guidance I
don't know where I'd be.

# *I* would like to take this opportunity to thank all those who helped make this book a reality.

Firstly to Samara and all of those at TinyLife. Your time and patience has been endless and without your support we wouldn't be here now!

To Jacqui my studio manager (and best friend) who is always there to help and keep me going with coffee and biscuits.

To Rotarian Paul Symonds and all the other Ballymena Rotarians who helped in so many ways.
Your input has been much appreciated.

To Jim Moreland, the worlds best black and white photographer for all his advice over the years.

To my granny Elliott for patiently knitting all the beautiful tiny hats.

To all the mums and dads I would like to say a big thank you for letting me share your very personal stories with the world.
Hopefully each one will give hope to those in the same circumstances.

And to all the little ones involved in the book. Without your amazing arrival we wouldn't have a story to tell.
There are not many people in this world who have as much fun in work as I do. I feel blessed to have had the pleasure of meeting each and every extraordinary one of you.

*Dawn McKeown* FRPS

There is nothing so precious than life itself
and nothing so vulnerable as a new born
tiny baby who can only
live and develop as a result of the
love, care, attention and
support of it's parents'.

~Sir. Nigel Hamilton
Vice President TinyLife

# About Dawn Mckeown Photography
## One of Ireland's leading child photographic studios

Based in Ballymena, Dawn Mckeown Photography specialises in child and family portraits. This low volume studio leaves lots of time for coffee, or a sleep and feed! The studio is completely child friendly from the moment you walk through the door and everything is set up to make the most nervous little one feel at ease.

Each family is totally unique and no two portraits look the same. The use of four backgrounds (including real brick and natural stone) and special child friendly lighting ensures that every portrait tells its own special story.

In 2011 Dawn McKeown was the first woman photographer in Ireland to receive a Fellowship from the professional panel of the prestigious Royal Photographic Society.

'There is nothing in this world as important as family.
Treasure every precious moment.'
Dawn Mckeown
Fellow of the Royal Photographic Society

Dawn McKeown Photography
12 John Street
Ballymena
BT43 6DX
028 2563 2816
www.dawnmckeownphotography.com
info@dawnmckeownphotography.com

Tiny Tales of Hope

# TinyLife is Northern Ireland's only premature and vulnerable baby charity.

TinyLife believe that it is the right of every family with a premature or sick baby to have access to a range of support services to meet their specific and sometimes very complex needs.

Over the years we at TinyLife have been privileged to be part of the story of most of the premature babies born in Northern Ireland. Throughout this unique journey we have talked to parents, listened to their worries, frustrations, and cried with them in times of despair. We have also been part of their hope and expectation for the joyful lives these little miracles have yet to achieve and have achieved. We have a special bond with all of them. Under ideal circumstances parenting is a challenging process however when an infant is admitted to a neonatal unit the stresses and challenges faced by parents is enhanced. The close relationship TinyLife has with families has enabled the charity to embark on service provision that meet the demands of families with premature and sick babies in Northern Ireland. TinyLife believe in a family centred approach to the support we offer and our unique service delivery ensures continuity of support for parents from hospital to home. The support offered by TinyLife is free of charge to families in Northern Ireland.

## Hospital based Support Service:

TinyLife Family Support Officers visit the neonatal units to offer parents support and information whist their premature or sick baby is still in hospital.

## Breast Pump Loan Service:

TinyLife provides electrical breast pumps for mums who wish to express their own milk to be fed to their baby while they are in neonatal care.

## Home Based Volunteer Support:

Our Family Support Officers match families with a trained volunteer who will provide practical, social and emotional support on a weekly basis.

## Dads Support:

Volunteer Dads are fathers of premature and sick babies who want to help other dad's going through the same experience. This is a one to one service based on matching the individual with a dad who has gone through a similar experience.

## Parent Support Groups:

These informal get-togethers provide an opportunity for parents who have been through similar experiences to receive support from one another and the Family Support Team. These meetings include talks by experts, baby massage, baby first aid and weaning.

## Baby Massage Courses:

During the year baby massage courses are held in various locations throughout Northern Ireland. These group sessions offer a wonderful experience for mothers and babies. For some parents unable to attend group sessions one to one courses are delivered at home.

## Resource Library:

TinyLife provides a range of books on premature birth and information leaflets relating to the development needs of premature, ill and disabled babies.

'Meeting the needs of families with premature babies provides us with daily challenges. We always want and need to do more. These beautiful babies are our next generation we must nurture them and help them fulfil their dreams.'

Deirdre Brady, Chief Executive TinyLife

33 Ballynahinch Road, Carryduff , Belfast BT8 8EH
Tel: 028 9081 5050
Fax: 028 9081 5850
 www.tinylife.org.uk
info@tinylife.org.uk

TinyLife Charity Number XN75792/1: Company Number NI037799

*Tiny Tales of Hope*

𝒫roduction of this book would not have been
possible without the kind support
of the following:

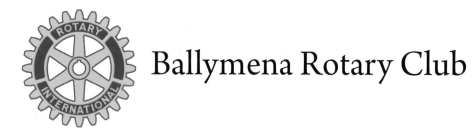 Ballymena Rotary Club